VOL. 139

CONTENTS

Cold Day in Hell

Words and Music by Gary Moore

Intro
Moderately ♩ = 101

Verse

1. So ___ man-y times, you tried to take the best of me.

Bridge

You __ nev - er lis - tened __ when I told you __

that __ you were way _____ out of line.

Too __ bus - y talk - in' to lis - ten, __

ac - cus - ing me ___ of tell - in' lies. _____

6

Guitar Solo

Verse

3. So ___ man-y times ___ you tried to ___ get the best of ___ me. ___

Spoken: Yes, you did.

So ___ man-y times, ___

Outro-Guitar Solo

F#9

C#m7

F#9

Begin fade

C#m7

8va

Fade out

loco

F#9

Oh Pretty Woman

Words and Music by A.C. Williams

*Bend both notes w/ same finger.

Can't make you love me

no mat-ter what I do.

Guitar Solo

Verse

3. Oh, pret-ty wom-an, that's al - right for you. __ Now you just   go on do-in'   what you

wan - na do. But some-day when you think _ that you've got it made, _ you'll get in

Chorus

Fm7

wa - ter deep _ e - nough so you can't wade. _ Pret - ty wom-an,

Cm7

what's the mat-ter with you? _____ Can't make you

G7#9

love me _ no mat - ter what I _____ do.

Bb5   B5   Cm7

P.M.   P.M. - - - -

Outro

Oh, pret - ty wom - an. _____   Oh,   pret - ty wom - an.

Oh, pret - ty wom - an. _____

Oh,   pret - ty   wom - an,   can't make you   love   me _____

Empty Rooms

Words and Music by Gary Moore and Neil Carter

Interlude

You hope that she will

The Loner

Words and Music by Gary Moore and Max Middleton

D

E

Since I Met You Baby

Words and Music by Gary Moore

Intro
Moderately fast ♩ = 155

Verse

1. I used to wake up ___ in the morn-in' ___ with an ach-in' head. ___ I

could-n't re-mem-ber an-y-thing I'd said. ___ My friends told me I was

*Sung as even eighth-notes.

met you, ba - by.　　　　　Since _ I _____ met you, ba - by.　　　　　Since _ I

*Sung as even eighth-notes.

met you, ba - by.　　　Since _ I　met you, ba - by,　I'm hap-py as a man __ could _

Guitar Solo

__ be. __ *Spoken:* One more time! __

grad. bend

*Played as even eighth-notes.

Outro-Chorus

Still Got the Blues

Words and Music by Gary Moore

1. Used to be so _____ eas - y _____ to give my heart _____

_____ a - way, _____ but I found out the hard _____ way _____ there's a

price _____ you have _____ to pay. _____ I _____ found out

that love _____ was no _____ friend of mine _____

Bm7♭5
E5
for I should have known time after time.
slight P.M.
Chorus
Am
Em7
Am
D9
So long, it was so long ago, but I've
F9
E7♯9
Am
N.C.
still got the blues for you.
Verse
Dm7
Dm7/G
Cmaj7
Fmaj7
2. Used to be so easy to fall in love again,

but I found out the ___ hard _ way   it's a road _____ that leads

to pain. ___   Well, I   found _ that love _____

was more _____ than ___ just a game, ___   you're play - in'

to win ___   but you'll   lose _____ just ___ the same. ___

emp - ty space ____ you __ used to be.

Guitar Solo

56

Texas Strut

Words and Music by Gary Moore

with the Tex - as Blues.

Interlude

The Tex - as Blues.

Verse

2. Got my - self in dou - ble trou -

ble when I saw that Tex - as flood. ___ Stev - ie

Interlude

A5

Blues.

Haw, haw, haw, haw.

Guitar Solo

A5

Huh.

let ring ----|

let ring ----|

let ring --------|

*Played as even eighth-notes.

64

B5

*Played as even eighth-notes.

Interlude

Walking by Myself

By James A. Lane

Verse

3. You know ____ I ____ love you. ____ You know ____ it's

true. ____ I'll give you all my... babe.

*Played as even eighth-notes.

GUITAR NOTATION LEGEND

THE MUSICAL STAFF shows pitches and rhythms and is divided by bar lines into measures. Pitches are named after the first seven letters of the alphabet.

TABLATURE graphically represents the guitar fingerboard. Each horizontal line represents a string, and each number represents a fret.

4th string, 2nd fret

1st & 2nd strings open, played together

open D chord

HALF-STEP BEND: Strike the note and bend up 1/2 step.

WHOLE-STEP BEND: Strike the note and bend up one step.

GRACE NOTE BEND: Strike the note and immediately bend up as indicated.

SLIGHT (MICROTONE) BEND: Strike the note and bend up 1/4 step.

BEND AND RELEASE: Strike the note and bend up as indicated, then release back to the original note. Only the first note is struck.

PRE-BEND: Bend the note as indicated, then strike it.

VIBRATO: The string is vibrated by rapidly bending and releasing the note with the fretting hand.

PALM MUTING: The note is partially muted by the pick hand lightly touching the string(s) just before the bridge.

HAMMER-ON: Strike the first (lower) note with one finger, then sound the higher note (on the same string) with another finger by fretting it without picking.

PULL-OFF: Place both fingers on the notes to be sounded. Strike the first note and without picking, pull the finger off to sound the second (lower) note.

LEGATO SLIDE: Strike the first note and then slide the same fret-hand finger up or down to the second note. The second note is not struck.

SHIFT SLIDE: Same as legato slide, except the second note is struck.

TRILL: Very rapidly alternate between the notes indicated by continuously hammering on and pulling off.

TAPPING: Hammer ("tap") the fret indicated with the pick-hand index or middle finger and pull off to the note fretted by the fret hand.

NATURAL HARMONIC: Strike the note while the fret-hand lightly touches the string directly over the fret indicated.

PINCH HARMONIC: The note is fretted normally and a harmonic is produced by adding the edge of the thumb or the tip of the index finger of the pick hand to the normal pick attack.

TREMOLO PICKING: The note is picked as rapidly and continuously as possible.

VIBRATO BAR DIVE AND RETURN: The pitch of the note or chord is dropped a specified number of steps (in rhythm), then returned to the original pitch.

VIBRATO BAR SCOOP: Depress the bar just before striking the note, then quickly release the bar.

VIBRATO BAR DIP: Strike the note and then immediately drop a specified number of steps, then release back to the original pitch.

Additional Musical Definitions

(accent)   • Accentuate note (play it louder).

(staccato)   • Play the note short.

D.S. al Coda   • Go back to the sign (𝄋), then play until the measure marked "*To Coda*," then skip to the section labelled "**Coda**."

D.C. al Fine   • Go back to the beginning of the song and play until the measure marked "*Fine*" (end).

Fill   • Label used to identify a brief melodic figure which is to be inserted into the arrangement.

N.C.   • Harmony is implied.

• Repeat measures between signs.

• When a repeated section has different endings, play the first ending only the first time and the second ending only the second time.

Grade

Acoustic Guitar Playing

Compiled and edited by
Tony Skinner and Laurence Harwood for

The Specialists in Guitar Education

RGT ®

Registry of Guitar Tutors

A CIP record for this publication is available from the British Library
ISBN: 978-1-905908-02-8

Printed and bound in Great Britain

Published by Registry Publications

Registry Mews, 11-13 Wilton Rd, Bexhill, Sussex, TN40 1HY

Compiled by

The Specialists in Guitar Education

RGT®

Registry of Guitar Tutors

www.RGT.org

Acknowledgements
The editors are grateful for the advice and support of all members of the RGT's
'Acoustic Guitar Advisory Panel' during the compilation of this series.

Cover design and photography by JAK Images; back cover photographs courtesy of Moon Guitars and Freshman Guitars.
Page 22 photograph supplied by John Hornby Skewes Ltd.

CONTENTS

INTRODUCTION

This publication is part of a progressive series of ten handbooks, primarily intended for candidates considering taking a Registry Of Guitar Tutors (RGT) examination in acoustic guitar playing. However, given each handbook's wide content of musical repertoire and associated educational material, the series provides a solid foundation of musical education for any acoustic guitar student – whether intending to take an examination or not.

Those preparing for an examination should use this handbook in conjunction with the Acoustic Guitar Exam Information Booklet and Acoustic Guitar Syllabus – both freely downloadable from the RGT website: www.RGT.org

NOTATION

In order that chords and scales can be made available for all to understand regardless of experience, they are illustrated in three formats: traditional notation, tablature and fretboxes – thereby ensuring that there is no doubt as to what is required. Each of these methods of notation is explained below.

TABLATURE

Horizontal lines represent the strings (with the top line being the high E string). The numbers on the string lines refer to the frets.
0 on a line means play that string open (unfretted). The example below means play at the second fret on the third string.

MUSICAL NOTATION

Each line, and space between lines, represents a different note. Leger lines are used to extend the stave for low or high notes.

A sharp (♯) before a note raises it by a half step (semitone), equivalent to one fret higher; a flat (♭) before a note lowers it by a half step, equivalent to one fret lower.

For scales at this grade, string and fret numbers are printed below the notation.

Fret-hand fingering is shown with the numbers **1 2 3 4**, with **0** indicating an open string. String numbers are shown in a circle.

The example shows the C major scale.

FRETBOXES

Vertical lines represent the strings – with the line furthest to the right representing the high E string.

Horizontal lines represent the frets.

The numbers on the lines show the recommended fingering. (**1** represents the index finger, **2** = the long middle finger, **3** = the ring finger, **4** = the little finger.)

This example means play with the second finger at the second fret on the G string:

FINGERING OPTIONS

The fingerings (including tablature positions) that have been chosen are those that are most likely to be effective for the widest range of players at this level. However, there is a variety of alternative fingerings that could be used, and any systematic and effective fingerings that produce a good musical result will be acceptable; there is no requirement to use the exact fingerings shown within this handbook. Throughout the examination, it is entirely the candidate's choice as to whether a pick (plectrum) or fingers are used to pick the strings. A thumbpick can be used if desired.

CD

A CD is supplied with this handbook as a learning aid and the recorded performances are designed specifically to provide an indication of the standard of playing expected at this grade.

TUNING

The use of an electronic tuner or other tuning aid, prior to or at the start of the examination, is permitted; candidates should be able to make any further adjustments, if required during the examination, unaided. The examiner will, upon request, offer an E or A note to tune to.

For examination purposes guitars should be tuned to Standard Concert Pitch (A=440Hz). A tuning guide is provided on the accompanying CD on Track 1.

EXAMINATION ENTRY

An examination entry form is provided at the back of this handbook. This is the only valid entry form for the RGT acoustic guitar examinations.

Please note that *if the entry form is detached and lost, it will not be replaced under any circumstances* and the candidate will be required to obtain a replacement handbook to obtain another entry form.

The entry form includes a unique entry code to enable you to enter online via the RGT website **www.RGT.org**

FINGERBOARD KNOWLEDGE

The examiner will choose a selection of the chords and scales shown in this chapter and ask the candidate to play them *from memory*. In addition, the examiner may ask the candidate to play any of the chords or scales from previous grades.

Chords and scales can be played using either the fingers or a pick (plectrum).

Overall, the examiner will be listening for accurate, clear and even playing. Prompt presentations, without undue delay or hesitation after being asked to play a chord or scale, will be taken as an indication of secure knowledge.

A maximum of 10 marks may be awarded in this section of the examination.

CHORDS

Chords should be played using a single slow strum, starting with the lowest (root) note. The whole chord shape should be carefully placed on the fingerboard before, and kept on during, playing.

Ensure that no required open strings are muted (these are marked with a **0** by the fretbox).

When playing a chord, a string which should not be sounded is marked with an **X** by the fretbox.

At this grade, some chords (F, Dm7, Dmaj7) are fretted using a partial (or half) barre, with the first finger laying flat and fretting more than one string.

CHORD SYMBOLS

This handbook (and examination) use the following standard abbreviations when referring to chords:

- The symbol for a major chord is the capital letter of the name of the chord. For example, the symbol for A major is **A**.
- The symbol for a minor chord is the capital letter of the name of the chord plus lower case **m**. For example, the symbol for A minor is **Am.**
- The symbol for a dominant seventh chord is the capital letter of the name of the chord followed by the number 7. For example, the symbol for A dominant 7 is **A7.**
- The symbol for a minor seventh chord is the capital letter of the name of the chord plus lower case m and the number 7. For example, the symbol for A minor 7 is **Am7.**
- The symbol for a major seventh chord is the capital letter of the name of the chord plus maj7. For example, the symbol for A major 7 is **Amaj7.**

The new chords set for Grade Two are:

- **F**   **• C7, G7**

- **Amaj7, Cmaj7, Dmaj7, Fmaj7, Gmaj7**   **• Am7, Dm7, Em7**

These chords are illustrated below.

Track 2   **LISTEN AND LEARN**   All of the set chords can be heard on CD track 2.

In addition, candidates will be expected to know the chords from lower grades:

- **A, C, D, E, G**   **• Am, Dm, Em**   **• A7, B7, D7, E7**

Candidates who are not familiar with any of these chords should study the previous handbooks in this series, as these chords may be used within the Performance, Accompaniment and Aural Assessment sections of the examination.

F major

F

C dominant 7

C7

G dominant 7

G7

A major 7

Amaj7

C major 7

Cmaj7

D major 7

Dmaj7

F major 7

Fmaj7

G major 7

Gmaj7

The 5th string is muted by allowing the 2nd finger to lightly rest upon it.

A minor 7

Am7

D minor 7

Dmin7

E minor 7

Em7

SCALES

Scales should be played ascending and descending, i.e. from the lowest note to the highest and back again without repeating, or pausing at, the top note. Scales should be played at an approximate tempo of 120 beats per minute. (This suggested tempo is for general guidance only and slightly slower or faster performances will be acceptable, providing that the tempo is maintained evenly throughout.)

The new requirements for Grade Two are:

- **A major scale – 2 octaves**
- **A Dorian modal scale – 2 octaves**

These are illustrated below.

In addition, candidates should be familiar with the one octave scales from lower grades:

- **C, G and D major** • **A natural minor**

A major scale – 2 octaves

A B C♯ D E F♯ G♯ A

A Dorian modal scale – 2 octaves

A B C D E F♯ G A

Track 3

LISTEN AND LEARN
All of the set scales can be heard on CD track 3.

PERFORMANCE

Candidates should select and play a total of TWO pieces comprised of ONE Rhythm Playing Study plus *either* ONE Fingerstyle Study *or* ONE melody.

Performances do not need to be from memory; the handbook may be used during this section of the exam. Candidates should remember to bring the handbook to the exam if not intending to play from memory; photocopies will not be permitted.

RHYTHM PLAYING STUDIES

The candidate must select and perform, using the prescribed strum pattern, ONE of the Rhythm Playing Studies in this chapter.

- Each study consists of an 8-bar chord progression that is played twice before ending on the key chord.

- After the repeat section, the final closing bar should be played with just a single strum.

- Tempo indications are for general guidance only.

- A pick (plectrum) is recommended but fingers, or fingers and a pick, can be used if preferred. Any combination of upstrokes and downstrokes is acceptable providing a good musical result is achieved.

- Providing the overall shape of the prescribed strum pattern is clearly portrayed, occasional use of stylistically appropriate additional 'ghost' notes, staccato or rests is permitted for interpretive purposes.

RHYTHM PLAYING ADVICE

A maximum of 25 marks may be awarded for the Rhythm Playing Study.

In order to achieve the most musical performance and obtain a high mark in the exam you should aim for the following when performing the Rhythm Playing Study:

- A secure knowledge of the chord shapes and the facility to change from one chord shape to another smoothly and without hesitation or delay.

- Clear sounding chords that are free of fretbuzz and any unintended muting of notes.

- A fluent rhythm style, maintaining an even tempo throughout.

- Accurate reproduction of the notated strum pattern.

- Accurate following of the dynamic marks.

Dynamic marks

These are symbols that indicate how loudly or softly you should play:

f = loudly

p = softly

◁ = gradually get louder

The set of two repeat dots ‖: :‖ indicates the section that should be repeated.

Rhythm Playing Study No. 1

Strum pattern:

♩. ♪ ♫♫

With movement

$\frac{4}{4}$ ‖: C |Cmaj7 |Dm7 |Fmaj7 |Em |Am7 |F |G7   :‖ C   ‖
f   *p*   ◁   *f*

The notated strum pattern ♩. ♪ ♫♫ indicates that you should play on the following

underlined beats: <u>**1**</u> er & a 2 er <u>**&**</u> a <u>**3**</u> <u>**er**</u> <u>**&**</u> a <u>**4**</u> er & a

Track
4   **LISTEN AND LEARN**
Rhythm Playing Study No. 1 can be heard on CD track 4

Rhythm Playing Study No. 2

Strum pattern:

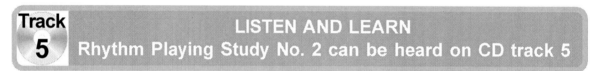

Fairly slow

$\frac{3}{4}$ ‖: **Am** |**Am7** |**Dm** |**Dm7** |**F** |**G** |**Em** |**E7** :‖ **Am** ‖

p   *f*

This study is in $\frac{3}{4}$ time – meaning that there are three main beats per bar.

The notated strum pattern ♪· ♫ ♫ ♪ indicates that you should play on the following

underlined beats: <u>**1**</u> er & <u>a</u> <u>**2**</u> er <u>**&**</u> a <u>**3**</u> er & a

Track 5   LISTEN AND LEARN
Rhythm Playing Study No. 2 can be heard on CD track 5

Rhythm Playing Study No. 3

Strum pattern:

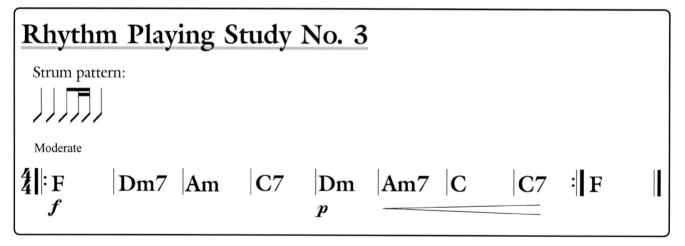

Moderate

$\frac{4}{4}$ ‖: **F** |**Dm7** |**Am** |**C7** |**Dm** |**Am7** |**C** |**C7** :‖ **F** ‖

f   *p*

This study is in $\frac{4}{4}$ time – meaning that there are four main beats per bar.

The notated strum pattern ♪ ♪ ♫ ♫ ♪ indicates that you should play on the following

underlined beats: <u>**1**</u> er & a <u>**2**</u> er & a <u>**3**</u> er <u>**&**</u> <u>a</u> <u>**4**</u> er & a

Track 6   LISTEN AND LEARN
Rhythm Playing Study No. 3 can be heard on CD track 6

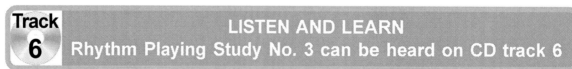

Candidates can choose to play *either*: one of the following Fingerstyle Studies, OR a melody from the next section in this chapter.

FINGERSTYLE STUDIES

- Each fingerstyle study consists of an 8-bar notated chord progression that incorporates a common fingerstyle pattern.

- The study should be played twice before ending on the key chord.

- Tempo indications are for general guidance only.

- Chord symbols are provided as an aid to study and performance. It is recommended that you finger the entire chord shape even if certain strings are not intended to be used: this has the benefit that if you accidentally strike an unrequired string it may still fit with the other notes being played.

- Pick-hand fingering is indicated as follows: **p** = thumb, **i** = index finger, **m** = middle finger, **a** = third finger. The pick-hand fingering shown on the notation is recommended as it is likely to be the most effective for the widest range of players at this level, however there is a variety of alternative fingerings that could be used and any systematic and effective fingerings that produce a good musical result will be acceptable.

FINGERSTYLE ADVICE

A maximum of 25 marks may be awarded for the Fingerstyle Study.

In order to achieve the most musical performance and obtain a high mark in the exam, you should aim for the following when performing the Fingerstyle Study:

- Accurate reproduction of the notated fingerstyle pattern.

- Secure knowledge of the chord shapes used and the ability to keep all the required notes sounding clearly.

- A fluent picking style, maintaining an even tempo throughout.

- The ability to change smoothly from one chord shape to another without cutting off notes from the previous bar early.

Fingerstyle Study No. 1

This study uses the fingering pattern **pimami** throughout. This means that you should start with the thumb playing the bass note, the treble strings are then picked with the fingers from the third string to the first string and back again.

Track 7

LISTEN AND LEARN
Fingerstyle Study No. 1 can be heard on CD track 7

Fingerstyle Study No. 2

This study uses the fingering pattern **pimiaimi** throughout. This means that you should start with the thumb playing the bass note, the index finger then picks the third string, the middle finger then picks the second string, followed by the index finger again picking the third string. The second half of each bar is identical except that the bass note is replaced by the third finger picking the first string.

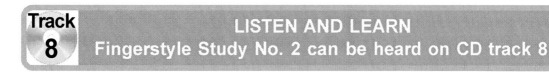

MELODIES

If not performing a fingerstyle study, candidates can instead select and perform ONE of the four traditional melodies that follow in this chapter or, if preferred, the melody can be a 'free choice' by the candidate of any other well-known melody from 1960 onwards – providing it is of at least similar technical standard and duration to the melodies below. (Whenever possible, candidates should bring the notation of the free choice melody to the exam for the examiner to view.) Melodies can be played with a pick or using fingers, as preferred by the candidate.

Chord symbols are provided for each melody in this handbook purely to enable a teacher or fellow player to provide accompaniment during practice. Candidates are NOT required to play the chords in the exam – only the melody, unaccompanied. (On the CD an accompaniment is played with the melody to enhance the musical effect and reinforce the timing for learning purposes.)

Tempo markings have been chosen that reflect the capabilities expected at this level, but are for general guidance only: faster, or slightly slower, tempos can be used providing they produce an effective musical result.

MELODY PLAYING ADVICE

A maximum of 25 marks may be awarded in the melody playing section of the exam.

As the melodies are based on the scales set for the Fingerboard Knowledge section of the exam (including the D major and A natural minor scales from Grade one), practising these scales will make learning the melodies much easier.

In order to achieve the most musical performance and obtain a high mark in the exam you should aim for the following when performing the melodies:

• An accurate reproduction of the pitch and rhythm of the melody.

• A fluent rendition, maintaining an even tempo throughout.

• Capturing the phrasing within the melody.

• Clear sounding notes that are free of fretbuzz.

Scarborough Fair

This melody is in $\frac{3}{4}$ time and is derived from the A Dorian modal scale.

Chord symbols are provided purely to enable a teacher or fellow player to provide accompaniment during practice. Candidates are NOT expected to play these chords in this section of the exam.

Track 9

LISTEN AND LEARN
Scarborough Fair can be heard on CD track 9

The Skye Boat Song

This melody is in $\frac{6}{8}$ time, also called 'compound duple' time, which means that each bar has two main beats, each divided into three. Another characteristic of this melody, which is notated in the key of A major, is the use of dotted rhythms, which give it a distinctive lilt.

The marking 'D.C. al Fine' means repeat from the beginning up until the end of bar 8, marked 'Fine' (i.e. 'the end').

Track 10

LISTEN AND LEARN
The Skye Boat Song can be heard on CD track 10.

House Of The Rising Sun

This melody is in $\frac{6}{8}$ time, and this arrangement uses notes from the A natural minor scale. A change in fret-hand position is required to reach the high A notes in bars 5 and 9.

Track 11

LISTEN AND LEARN
House Of The Rising Sun can be heard on CD track 11.

Londonderry Air

This arrangement © copyright 2007 by Registry Publications.

This melody, used in the popular song *Danny Boy*, is in $\frac{4}{4}$ time and is notated here in the key of D major. Notice how each phrase starts with a 'pick-up' of three eighth notes; this gives structure to what is quite a long melody.

Track 12

LISTEN AND LEARN
Londonderry Air can be heard on CD track 12.

MUSICAL KNOWLEDGE

The examiner will ask a range of questions, from the topics listed below, to test the candidate's knowledge of the anatomy of the guitar.

NOTES ON THE FINGERBOARD

Candidates may be asked to name any note taken from the scales set for this and previous grades. A summary of these is given below.

Fret

String	0	1	2	3	4	5
1	E	(F)	F♯(G♭)	G	G♯(A♭)	A
2	B	C	C♯(D♭)	D	(D♯/ E♭)	(E)
3	G	G♯(A♭)	A	(A♯/ B♭)	(B)	(C)
4	D	(D♯/ E♭)	E	F	F♯(G♭)	(G)
5	A	(A♯/ B♭)	B	C	C♯(D♭)	(D)
6	(E)	(F)	(F♯ / G♭)	(G)	(G♯/ A♭)	(A)

The notes shown in brackets do not occur in any of the set scales for this and previous grades, and are provided here only for completeness; knowledge of these will not be tested in the exam.

PARTS OF THE GUITAR

Candidates should be able to demonstrate knowledge of the anatomy of the acoustic guitar by being able to identify the location of the parts of the guitar shown on the illustration overleaf.

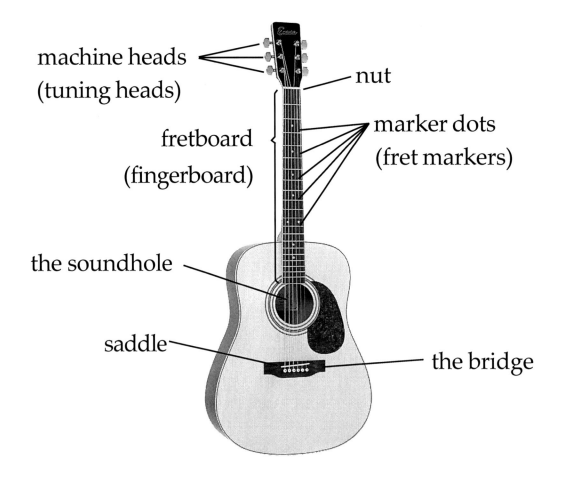

machine heads (tuning heads)

nut

fretboard (fingerboard)

marker dots (fret markers)

the soundhole

saddle

the bridge

MUSICAL KNOWLEDGE ADVICE

A maximum of 10 marks may be awarded in this section of the exam.

Knowing the names of the notes on the fingerboard helps to provide a secure musical foundation. Knowledge of the names of the main parts of the guitar will also prove useful when communicating with other guitarists. Being able to demonstrate secure knowledge in all of these areas will help you gain a high mark in this section of the exam.

In order to gain the highest marks, responses to the examiner's questions should be prompt and confident – demonstrating that the answers are known, rather than guessed or worked out.

ACCOMPANIMENT

In this section of the exam, the candidate should play a chordal accompaniment while the examiner plays an eight-bar melody (either live on guitar or keyboard, or via a recording).

- The candidate will be shown a chord chart for the melody. The examiner will then give a one bar count-in and play the melody once for the candidate to listen to without playing along.

- The examiner will then give another one bar count-in and the melody will be played a further three times without stopping. The candidate can accompany the first of these three verses if they wish to, but only the accompaniment of the second and third verses will be assessed.

It is recommended that during the first (unassessed) accompaniment verse a chord is strummed on the first beat of each bar so that the timing can be established. Alternatively, the candidate may prefer just to read through the chord chart and listen as the examiner plays the first verse of melody.

At this grade, there will be five different chords in the accompaniment chord chart, three of which will last for two bars. The range of chords will be restricted to the chords required for this and previous grades. The final chord (after the repeat) should be played with a single strum. The time signature will be $\frac{4}{4}$.

The style of the accompaniment is left to the candidate's discretion, and the candidate can chose to either strum or fingerpick. The CD recording that comes with this book provides an indication of the technical level that would be expected for a high mark at this grade – only the two assessed verses are provided for each example. It is NOT intended that candidates copy the style of accompaniments performed on the CD recording – these are provided purely as examples of the standard required – and candidates are strongly encouraged to devise their own rhythmic/picking styles; these should always relate to the style and timing of the melody played by the examiner.

The melody notation played by the examiner will not be seen by the candidate.

ACCOMPANIMENT ADVICE

A maximum of 20 marks may be awarded in this section of the exam.

In order to achieve the most musical performance and obtain a high mark in the exam you should aim for the following when performing your accompaniment:

- Remember that the very first time the examiner plays the melody, you have the chance to listen to it without needing to play along. Use this opportunity to listen carefully and try to absorb the melodic shape and structure of the melody.

- In the first verse of the three continuous playings your playing will not be assessed, so you can best use this time by reading through the chord chart and just strumming once on the first beat of each bar so that the timing becomes clearly fixed in your mind.

- In the remaining two verses use an appropriate rhythm or picking style that suits the mood, style and timing of the melody.

- Keep listening to the melody while playing your accompaniment and make sure to keep in time with it. Use your knowledge of the chord shapes to change smoothly from one chord to another, whilst making sure your chords ring clear.

- Try to include some variation in your performance.

Two examples of the *type* of test that will occur are given on the following pages. Note that each of the Accompaniment Examples is provided only as a sample of the *type* of melody and chord symbols that may occur in the exam.

Accompaniment Example 1

Chord chart

| $\frac{4}{4}$: Am | | Am | | Dm7 | | Dm7 | |

| G | | G | | F | | E | :|| Am | |

Melody

♩ = 120

Accompaniment Example 2

Chord chart

| $\frac{4}{4}$ ‖: Dmaj7 | Dmaj7 | Em | Em |

| G | G | A | A7 :‖ Dmaj7 ‖

Melody

♩ = 92

Track 14

LISTEN AND LEARN
Accompaniment Example 2 can be heard on CD track 14.

AURAL ASSESSMENT

T he candidate will be given a selection of rhythm, pitch and harmony tests. The examiner will play these either on guitar or keyboard (live or via a recording). Examples of the tests are provided below; these are also included on the accompanying CD.

A maximum of 10 marks may be awarded in total during this section of the examination.

RHYTHM TESTS

The examiner will twice play a four bar melody in either $\frac{3}{4}$ or $\frac{4}{4}$ time. The rhythm may include dotted notes, but will not include any notes shorter than eighth notes (quavers).

Test a) During the second playing the candidate should clap or tap the main pulse, accenting the first beat of each bar.

Test b) The candidate should then identify the time signature as either $\frac{3}{4}$ or $\frac{4}{4}$ time.

Test c) The examiner will play any ONE bar of the melody twice. The candidate should reproduce the exact rhythm by clapping or tapping.

Three examples demonstrating the *type* of rhythm tests that will occur at this grade are shown below.

Example 1 (CD track 15)

Example 2 (CD track 16)

Test A & B

Candidate claps:

Test C

Candidate claps:

Example 3 (CD track 17)

Test A & B

Candidate claps:

Test C

Candidate claps:

PITCH AND HARMONY TESTS

Test d) The candidate should look away while the examiner plays a four-note phrase consisting of notes taken from the C major scale. The phrase will start on the keynote. The examiner will play the phrase twice before the candidate makes a first attempt to reproduce the phrase on the guitar. If required, the candidate can request the examiner to play the phrase one further time, prior to the candidate's second attempt. However, the candidate will then be expected to reproduce the phrase promptly and will not be permitted any further attempts at 'working it out'. Some examples of the *type* of phrase are shown below. These can be heard on CD track 18.

Example 1

Example 2

Example 3

Example 4

Test e) The candidate should look away while the examiner plays a short chord progression containing exclusively either major, minor, dominant seventh, major seventh or minor seventh chords. The candidate will then be asked to identify the *type* of chord that was played. Below are some examples of the style of test:

Example 1 (CD track 19)

$\frac{2}{4}$ ‖ A | D | E | A ‖ = major

Example 2 (CD track 20)

$\frac{2}{4}$ ‖ Am | Dm | Em | Am ‖ = minor

Example 3 (CD track 21)

$\frac{2}{4}$ ‖ A7 | D7 | E7 | A7 ‖ = dominant seventh

Example 4 (CD track 22)

$\frac{2}{4}$ ‖Amaj7|Dmaj7|Dmaj7|Amaj7‖ = major seventh

Example 5 (CD track 23)

$\frac{2}{4}$ ‖Am7 |Dm7 |Em7 |Am7 ‖ = minor seventh

RGT
Registry of Guitar Tutors

EXAMINATION ENTRY FORM
ACOUSTIC GUITAR
GRADE TWO

ONLINE ENTRY – AVAILABLE FOR UK CANDIDATES ONLY

For **UK candidates**, entries and payments can be made online at www.RGT.org, using the entry code below. You will be able to pay the entry fee by credit or debit card at a secure payment page on the website.

Your unique and confidential examination entry code is:

AB-5491-CF

Keep this unique code confidential, as it can only be used once. Once you have entered online, you should sign this form overleaf. **You must bring this signed form to your exam and hand it to the examiner in order to be admitted to the exam room.**

If NOT entering online, please complete BOTH sides of this form and return to the address overleaf.

SESSION (Spring/Summer/Winter): _____ YEAR: _____

Dates/times NOT available: _____

Note: Only name *specific* dates (and times on those dates) when it would be <u>absolutely impossible</u> for you to attend due to important prior commitments (such as pre-booked overseas travel) which cannot be cancelled. We will then endeavour to avoid scheduling an exam session in your area on those dates. In fairness to all other candidates in your area, **only list dates on which it would be impossible for you to attend.** An entry form that blocks out unreasonable periods may be returned. (Exams may be held on any day of the week including, but not exclusively, weekends. Exams may be held within or outside of the school term.)

Candidate Details: *Please write as clearly as possible using BLOCK CAPITALS*

Candidate Name (as to appear on certificate): _____

Address: _____

_____ Postcode: _____

Tel. No. (day): _____ (mobile): _____

IMPORTANT: Please take care to write your email address below *as clearly as possible* as your exam entry acknowledgement and your exam appointment details will be sent to this email address.
Only provide an email address that is in regular monitored use.

Email:_____

Where an email address is provided your exam correspondence will be sent by email only, and not by post. This will ensure your exam correspondence will reach you sooner.

Teacher Details *(if applicable)*

Teacher Name (as to appear on certificate): _____

RGT Tutor Code (if applicable):_____

Address: _____

_____ Postcode: _____

Tel. No. (day): _____ (mobile): _____

Email:_____

RGT Acoustic Guitar Official Entry Form

**The standard LCM entry form is NOT valid for Acoustic Guitar exam entries.
Entry to the examination is only possible via this original form.
Photocopies of this form will not be accepted under *any* circumstances.**

- Completion of this entry form is an agreement to comply with the current syllabus requirements and conditions of entry published at www.RGT.org. Where candidates are entered for examinations by a teacher, parent or guardian that person hereby takes responsibility that the candidate is entered in accordance with the current syllabus requirements and conditions of entry.

- If you are being taught by an *RGT registered* tutor, please hand this completed form to your tutor and request him/her to administer the entry on your behalf.

- For candidates with special needs, a letter giving details should be attached.

Examination Fee: £_____   Late Entry Fee (if applicable): £_____

Total amount submitted: £_____

Cheques or postal orders should be made payable to Registry of Guitar Tutors.

Details of conditions of entry, entry deadlines and examination fees are obtainable from the RGT website: www.RGT.org

Once an entry has been accepted, entry fees cannot be refunded.

CANDIDATE INFORMATION (UK Candidates only)

In order to meet our obligations in monitoring the implementation of equal opportunities policies, UK candidates are required to supply the information requested below. *The information provided will in no way whatsoever influence the marks awarded during the examination.*

Date of birth: _____ Age: _____ Gender – please circle: male / female

Ethnicity (please enter 2 digit code from chart below): _____ Signed: _____

ETHNIC ORIGIN CLASSIFICATIONS (If you prefer not to say, write '17' in the space above.)

White: **01 British**   **02 Irish**   **03 Other white background**

Mixed: **04 White & black Caribbean**   **05 White & black African**   **06 White & Asian**   **07 Other mixed background**

Asian or Asian British: **08 Indian**   **09 Pakistani**   **10 Bangladeshi**   **11 Other Asian background**

Black or Black British: **12 Caribbean**   **13 African**   **14 Other black background**

Chinese or Other Ethnic Group: **15 Chinese**   **16 Other**   **17 Prefer not to say**

I understand and accept the current syllabus regulations and conditions of entry for this examination as specified on the RGT website.

Signed by candidate (if aged 18 or over) _____ Date _____

If candidate is under 18, this form should be signed by a parent/guardian/teacher (circle which applies):

Signed _____ Name _____ Date_____

UK ENTRIES

See overleaf for details of how to enter online OR return this form to:
Registry of Guitar Tutors, Registry Mews, 11 to 13 Wilton Road, Bexhill-on-Sea, E. Sussex, TN40 1HY
(If you have submitted your entry online do NOT post this form, instead you need to sign it above and hand it to the examiner on the day of your exam.)
To contact the RGT office telephone 01424 222222 or Email office@RGT.org

NON-UK ENTRIES

To locate the address within your country that entry forms should be sent to, and to view exam fees in your currency, visit the RGT website **www.RGT.org** and navigate to the 'RGT Worldwide' section.